OLLIE'S LOST KITTEN

NICOLA KILLEN

Lond   Iew Delhi

It was a crisp autumn morning and
Ollie was heading outside to play,
closely followed by her cat, Pumpkin.

Miaow!

Ollie was about to jump
into a pile of leaves, when
she noticed it was moving!

She tried to take a closer look
but suddenly the wind whistled,

blowing the leaves
EVERYWHERE.

Hiding underneath was a little shivering kitten.

Ollie scooped the kitten into her arms and cuddled him until he felt warm.

The little kitten was very friendly and soon the three of them were playing together.

They started with a game of hide-and-seek,

"1...2...3...4...5..."

before catching falling leaves

and being explorers!

After so much excitement,
it was time for a rest.

But it wasn't long until the little kitten wanted to play again!

Ollie was having so much fun she forgot about Pumpkin napping under the tree . . .

and ran further and
further into the woods.

When the new friends reached the heart of the woods,
Ollie noticed there were posters everywhere.
She looked closer and saw a familiar face staring back . . .

It was the kitten and someone was looking for him!

"I need to take you home," Ollie whispered. "Do you know where that is?"

The kitten miaowed and suddenly the wind whistled, whipping hundreds of leaves into the air.

As the leaves settled, they revealed a secret path.

The kitten set off straight away,
with Ollie close behind.

Where would it lead them?

It was the kitten's home!

Ollie waved goodbye. She felt sad, but knew the kitten had someone who loved him just as much as she loved ... Pumpkin!

"Oh, Pumpkin," sobbed Ollie as she realised she'd left her own cat behind.

She hurried back through the
woods, unsure of the way,

not noticing the sky getting
darker and darker.

Lost and alone, Ollie sat down.

As a tear trickled down her cheek,
she heard a rustle in the leaves...

... and a familiar **miaow**!

"Pumpkin! You found me!
I'm so sorry I left you behind."

Purring loudly, Ollie's cat led
her out of the woods

and towards home.

That night, Ollie wasn't the only one happy to be reunited with their cat.

And in the morning, Ollie opened the door
to find a very special thank you gift!